Let's Pa... Brown

Charles M. Schulz

Selected cartoons from
KISS HER, YOU BLOCKHEAD!
Volume 2

CORONET BOOKS
Hodder and Stoughton

PEANUTS Comic Strips by Charles M. Schulz

Copyright © 1982 by United Feature Syndicate, Inc.

First published in the United States of America in 1985
by Ballantine Books
Coronet edition 1986

British Library C.I.P.

Schulz, Charles M.
 [Kiss her you blockhead. *Selections*] Let's party, Charlie
Brown : selected cartoons from Kiss her you
blockhead volume 2.
 I. [Kiss her you blockhead. *Selections*]
 II. Title
 741.5'973   PN6728.P4

 ISBN 0–340–39022–0

Printed and bound in Great Britain for
Hodder and Stoughton Paperbacks, a
division of Hodder and Stoughton Ltd.,
Mill Road, Dunton Green, Sevenoaks,
Kent (Editorial Office: 47 Bedford
Square, London, WC1B 3DP) by
Cox & Wyman Ltd., Reading.

Let's Party, CHARLIE BROWN

THERE'S THAT LITTLE RED-HAIRED GIRL STANDING IN THIS SAME LINE FOR THE MOVIES

GO AHEAD, AND STAND WITH HER...DON'T BE SO WISHY-WASHY...

I'LL JUST STAND HERE WITH MY SWEET BABBOO...

I'M NOT YOUR SWEET BABBOO!

BUT I'M SURE WISHY-WASHY!

MOM SAID OUR DINNER WON'T BE READY FOR A FEW MINUTES...

GO AHEAD, AND START.. DON'T WAIT FOR US!

HOW THOUGHTFUL..

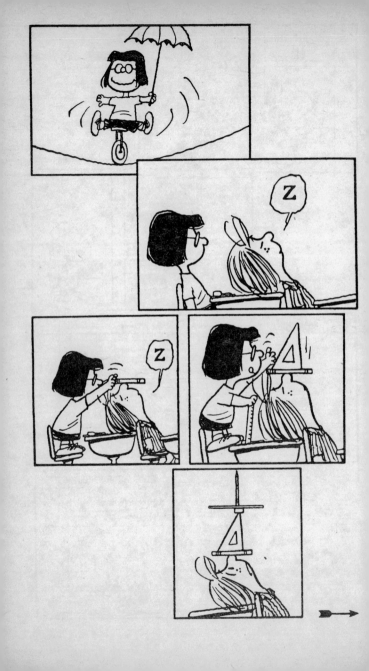

MANAGER'S OFFICE
THE BUCK STARTS
HERE.....

OKAY, TEAM, LET'S
PAY ATTENTION!

LAST YEAR WE HAD TOO
MANY PLAYERS GETTING HIT
ON THE HEAD WITH FLY BALLS...

LET'S SEE IF WE CAN'T
CHANGE THAT THIS YEAR

WHAP!

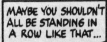

THE SULKER IS [IN]

SLAM!

GET OUT OF MY BEANBAG...I WANT TO SULK

GO SULK IN A DINING ROOM CHAIR

TWO OUTS ALREADY.. I CAN'T STAND IT!

OKAY, LUCY, WE NEED A RUN..HERE'S WHAT I WANT YOU TO DO...

IF YOU GET ON FIRST, WATCH FOR MY SIGNAL TO STEAL SECOND...I'LL TUG MY EAR LIKE THIS...

NOW, IF YOU GET TO SECOND, AND I WANT YOU TO STEAL AGAIN, I'LL CLAP MY HANDS LIKE THIS...

IF YOU GET TO THIRD, AND I WANT YOU TO STAY THERE, I'LL TUG MY OTHER EAR LIKE THIS, BUT IF I WANT YOU TO TRY TO STEAL HOME, I'LL RUB THE FRONT OF MY SHIRT...

STRIKE ONE!

STRIKE TWO!

STRIKE THREE!!

THAT WAS EASIER THAN TRYING TO REMEMBER ALL THOSE SIGNALS!

GO AHEAD, SIR..IT CAN'T HURT TO ASK...

MA'AM, ABOUT THIS "D MINUS" ON MY REPORT CARD...

"D" IS CERTAINLY A WONDERFUL LETTER.. IT'S PROBABLY ONE OF THE MOST IMPORTANT LETTERS IN OUR ALPHABET..BY ITSELF, IT HAS DIGNITY...

WHEN YOU PUT A "MINUS" IN FRONT OF IT, HOWEVER, IT LOSES THAT DIGNITY... IT APPEARS DRAINED..

PUT A "PLUS" IN FRONT OF THAT "D," MA'AM, AND IT CHANGES COMPLETELY! YOU'VE PLACED A SWORD IN ITS HAND THAT GIVES IT POWER AND STRENGTH !!!

I SEE...NO, THAT'S ALL RIGHT.. I UNDERSTAND...

SHE SAID SHE COULDN'T CHANGE MY GRADE...

BUT SHE SAID IF SHE'S EVER ON TRIAL FOR HER LIFE, SHE'D WANT ME FOR HER ATTORNEY...

He didn't get back
for three weeks.

HA HA HA HA HA

KLUNK!   KLUNK!

LEO TOLSTOY
WOULD HAVE BEEN
SO JEALOUS...

SCHULZ

YOU DIDN'T SAY ANYTHING ABOUT JOANNE CARNER, OR SALLY LITTLE, OR HOLLIS STACY, OR BILLIE JEAN KING, OR ROSIE CASALS OR SHARON WALSH! AND WHAT ABOUT DONNA ADAMEK, BETH HEIDEN OR MARY DECKER?

DID YOU TELL US WHAT CONNI PLACE HAS BEEN DOING? AND HOW ABOUT ALISON ROWE, AND TRACY CAULKINS, AND KAREN ROGERS, AND EVELYN ASHFORD, AND ANN MEYERS, AND JUDY SLADKY AND SARAH DOCTER?!

DID YOU SAY ANYTHING ABOUT JENNIFER HARDING OR SHIRLEY MULDOWNEY? WHAT DO YOU MEAN, "THAT'S SPORTS"?!!

WHAT DO YOU WANT TO WATCH NEXT, SIR? THERE'RE SOME OLD MOVIES ON THE OTHER CHANNELS..

"THE MEN," "A MAN FOR ALL SEASONS" AND "ALL THE KING'S MEN"

I CAN'T STAND IT...

"And then appeared upon the scene the only man I have ever met...without a single redeeming virtue save courage."

"Beau Geste"

AND KEEP A SHARP LOOKOUT!

HERE'S THE WORLD FAMOUS SERGEANT-MAJOR OF THE FOREIGN LEGION GUARDING FORT ZINDERNEUF WITH A PAWFUL OF MISERABLE RECRUITS

WHAT'S THAT? THERE! IN THE DISTANCE! SOMETHING IS MOVING!

GET READY, MEN..HERE COMES THE ENEMY!

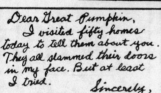

YES, MA'AM, THIS IS A LOOSE-LEAF BINDER THAT I HAVE ON MY HEAD

WELL, YOU SEE, IT WAS RAINING ON MY WAY TO SCHOOL THIS MORNING..

NO, MA'AM, I REALLY CAN'T TAKE IT OFF BECAUSE..

I HEARD SOMEONE ON TV SAY THAT THE WORLD IS GETTING WORSE EVERY DAY

THAT'S RIDICULOUS!

READY?

" DEAR SANTA CLAUS...I DON'T SUPPOSE YOU'VE EVER RECEIVED A LETTER BEFORE FROM A BIRD AND A DOG...HA HA ...ANYWAY, WE JUST THOUGHT WE'D DROP YOU A LINE "

READ THAT BACK, WILL YOU, PLEASE, SO I CAN HEAR HOW IT SOUNDS..

PUT AWAY THAT HISTORY BOOK, MARCIE... ART IS NEXT!

I LOVE ART CLASS!

HOW'S THIS, MA'AM? TWENTY-FOUR COWS STANDING IN A PASTURE.. EACH ONE RENDERED IN EXQUISITE DETAIL!

MAYBE I'LL ADD SOME SHEEP, AND RABBITS AND SQUIRRELS...

➡

SOMEBODY CHECK THE SHORTSTOP TO SEE IF HE'S AWAKE!

HEY, WAKE UP!

I SHOULD HAVE LET HIM SLEEP...AS SOON AS HE WAKES UP, HE WANTS A GLASS OF ORANGE JUICE!

THE COURT WILL NOT AID THOSE WHO HAVE COMMITTED ILLEGAL ACTS IN A MATTER...

..AND THEN ASK THE COURT'S HELP TO RECOVER FOR ANY INJURY THEY MAY HAVE SUFFERED AS A RESULT THEREOF!

RATS!

THIS IS OUR BIGGEST GAME OF THE SEASON

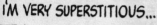

I'M VERY SUPERSTITIOUS...

ON THE MORNING OF OUR BIGGEST GAME, I ALWAYS POUR MYSELF A BOWL OF THE SAME KIND OF CEREAL...

AND I'M ALWAYS TOO NERVOUS TO EAT...

CHARLIE BROWN – A SELECTION

All these books are available at your local bookshop or newsagent, or can be ordered direct from the publisher. Just tick the titles you want and fill in the form below.

Prices and availability subject to change without notice.

Hodder & Stoughton Paperbacks, P.O. Box 11, Falmouth, Cornwall.

Please send cheque or postal order, and allow the following for postage and packing:

U.K. – 55p for one book, plus 22p for the second book, and 14p for each additional book ordered up to a £1.75 maximum.

B.F.P.O. and EIRE – 55p for the first book, plus 22p for the second book, and 14p per copy for the next 7 books, 8p per book thereafter.

OTHER OVERSEAS CUSTOMERS – £1.00 for the first book, plus 25p per copy for each additional book.

Name ....

Address ....

....